My Bible Story Book of
ABC'S

Books in this Series

My Adam and Eve Book of Opposites
My Noah's Ark Book of Colors
My Baby Jesus Book of Numbers
My Bible Story Book of ABC's

Copyright © 1995 by Educational Publishing Concepts, Inc., Wheaton, Illinois

Published by Concordia Publishing House
3558 S. Jefferson Avenue, St. Louis, MO 63118-3968
Manufactured in the United States of America

1 2 3 4 5 6 7 8 9 10   04 03 02 01 00 99 98 97 96 95

My Bible Story Book of ABC'S

Glenda Palmer

Illustrated by
Rick Incrocci

CPH™
SAINT LOUIS

Aa

Adam was the first man God made. God asked Adam to name all the animals He made.

Bb Adam named **b**ears
and **b**eavers.

Cc He named **c**ats and **c**rocodiles. **Dd** He named **d**ogs and **d**onkeys.

Ee

Eve was Adam's wife. They lived in the Garden of Eden. God told Adam and Eve to have children.

The first two sons they had were named Cain and Abel.

Ff Adam and Eve and their two sons were a **f**amily.

Gg

God made everything in the world.
He made **g**rass and **g**rasshoppers and **g**rapes.

Hh He even made the **h**uge **h**ippopotamus.

Ii Isaac was the son of Abraham and Sarah.
Abraham and Sarah loved **I**saac.
Isaac's name means laughter.

Jj Joseph's mom and dad loved him.
His dad gave him a wonderful coat.
Joseph's brothers were jealous.
They sold him as a slave.

Kk God helped Joseph and kept him safe. He made Joseph almost as important as a **k**ing.

Ll Joseph **l**oved the **L**ord. He forgave his brothers.

Mm

When **Moses** was a baby, a princess found him floating in a basket in the river. **Moses** grew up in a palace and helped God's people. **Moses** loved God too.

Nn

One of the first stories in the Bible is about **N**oah.
God told **N**oah to build an ark.
Two of each kind of animal came onto the ark.

Oo Otters and ostriches.

Pp Porcupines, pigs, and penguins.

Qq And quail.

Rr

Then it began to **r**ain and **r**ain and **r**ain. But God kept Noah and all the animals safe and dry in the ark.

Ss
Samuel was a little boy who loved and obeyed God.

Tt Samuel lived in a special tent church called a tabernacle. One night God spoke to him there. Samuel listened to God.

Uu Samuel looked **u**p to listen to God. A shepherd boy named David looked **u**p to God too.

Vv With God, David won a **v**ictory.

Ww

Victory means **win**. God helped David **win** when he fought against the giant, Goliath.

Xx

God's people were excited when David killed Goliath.

Yy

God's people listened to Him and said **yes** when He asked them to do something. God talks to **you** in the Bible. He helps **you** to say **yes** to Him too. Adam said **yes** when God asked him to name the animals. He named this funny animal a **yak**.

Zz

Adam named the animals from **A** to **Z**, from **a**lligators to **z**ebras, and all the animals in between.

What does your name begin with? Point to the letter. Is it **A** for **A**shley? Is it **Z** for **Z**ach? Is it somewhere in between? It is just the right name for you.